Dear Young Friend:

   This book was written especially for you. It is a celebration of your life and family. We invite you to think about all the qualities, interests and skills that make you unique and special. Some of your qualities may include honesty, humor and patience. Your interests may vary from sports to cooking or from reading to bicycling. Your skills could include how well you throw a ball, draw a picture or listen to a grown-up. As you create various art projects, finish sentences and complete pictures, you will become the author of your own very special book. This will be a book all about you. We hope you will enjoy sharing this book with family and friends.

   Here is some information to help you create your new book. On each page, you will find a key that tells you what materials you will need and whether or not you will need the help of a grown-up you trust. After reading the materials list, make sure you ask permission of a grown-up before using supplies in your home. If you see a helping hand ✋ this means you should work with a grown-up to complete the activity on that page.

   Well, it is time to start! We are sure you will have a good time learning about yourself and your family as you complete this book. Do not forget that when you finish, you will have a book that is one of a kind — just as you are one of a kind.

Happy Creating!!!!

Dear Parent or Other Caring Adult:

Our goal in creating this activity book was to provide you with an avenue to learn more about your child and build his or her self-esteem. We consulted with both educators and parents. The educators we worked with brought to this project over 60 years' combined experience in the development of hands-on activities for children. We also asked parents to review and pilot each activity. We believe these steps have helped us to bring you a well-crafted activity book.

This book will be most effective in helping you learn about your child and boost the development of positive self-esteem if you take an active approach to using it. Start flipping through the book with your child. Discuss the various activities, see which ones most interest your child, and plan for ways that you can help. You may need to read many of the activities to a younger child. Note that the "helping hand" pictured with some activities indicates that your child may need your assistance to successfully complete that activity. You may want to discuss with your child a system for gathering materials for the various activities.

Remember that just by listening to your child, you are making a major impact on your child's self-esteem. When we listen to our children we make them feel valuable. We also recommend that you join in the creating and sharing of the various activities. Do not forget to congratulate your child each time an activity is completed. At the end of the book, you will find a list of activity variations and ways you can add to or go beyond the activities as they appear in the activity book.

Most of all, have fun loving and enjoying time with your special child!!

Happy Creating!!!!

P.S. You may pull out this letter and the activity variations page when your child has finished producing this book. It will then truly be a book created by your child!

Table of Contents

Answers to Anger

We all become angry sometimes. There are good and bad ways to deal with anger. Yelling and hitting are bad ways! Circle the actions below which help you calm down when you are angry. Then write in two other ways you can calm down when you're angry.

1,2,3...
count to ten

draw a picture

talk to a friend

take a walk

ride your bike

read a book

another way

TOYS

clean your room

write a letter

talk to the person who upset you

another way

You will need: a pencil

Certificate of Awesome Friendship

Happily awarded to _____

because _____

_____

_____

Given by your thankful friend _____

on this _____ day of _____ , 19____

Here is an Awesome Friendship Award. Do you feel lucky to have a special friend? If so, fill out this award, cut it out on the dotted lines, and award it to your good friend!

You will need: a pen or pencil, scissors

Badge of Pride

Everyone has skills and qualities to be proud of. However, sometimes our feelings are hurt when someone says something that makes us not feel so proud. When this happens, you might need a "Badge of Pride." Then you will remember how wonderful and neat you are!

Here is how to make a Badge of Pride:

1. Think of your best qualities. What makes you proud of yourself? What makes you special?

2. Draw pictures or write those words inside the badge below. You may color it if you wish.

3. Cut out your "Badge of Pride." Ask a grown-up for yarn or string to attach to the badge. Now you can wear your new badge around your neck.

4. Stand tall and be proud of yourself!

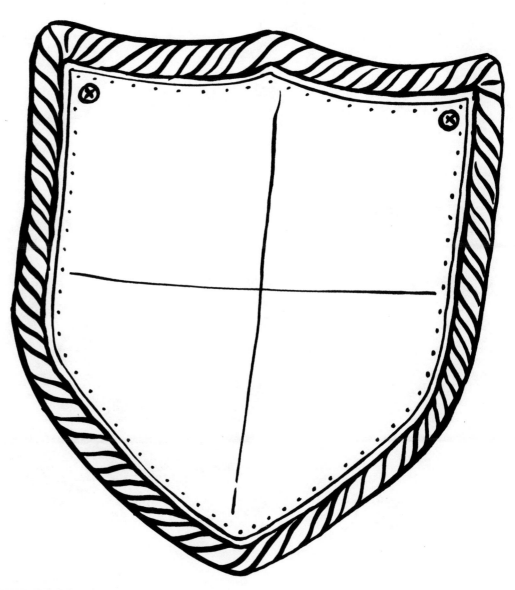

You will need: a pen or pencil, scissors, yarn or string

Just when you think everything is going fine, your day can be ruined by a bully. It is a good idea to practice ahead of time what you could do and say if someone were bullying you.

What to do:

1. Ask a friend or family member to help practice this scene.

2. Pretend a bully is teasing and bugging you. You are tired of this, and you wish he or she would stop. Try the following:

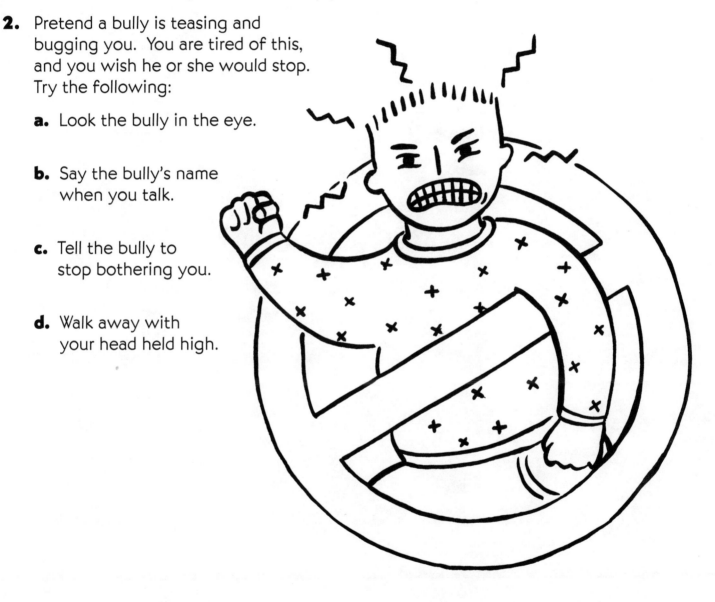

   a. Look the bully in the eye.

   b. Say the bully's name when you talk.

   c. Tell the bully to stop bothering you.

   d. Walk away with your head held high.

You will need: a friend or family member

Collage Creation

A collage is a collection of pictures or art pieces. You can make an incredible collage creation by following the directions below. It will make you feel good whenever you look at it.

What to do:

1. Ask your family for permission to cut pictures from magazines.

2. Cut out any pictures that make you feel happy, make you smile, remind you of funny things, or show people looking happy.

3. Glue the pictures onto the next page or a piece of construction paper. Cover the whole piece of paper so you have a true "collage."

4. Share your creative collage with your family and friends, telling them why the pictures make you happy.

You will need: magazines, scissors and glue.

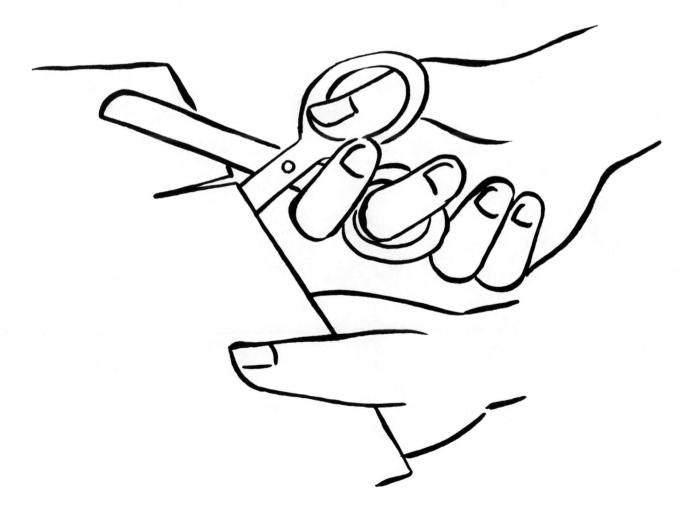

Creative Composer

_____

_____

_____

_____

_____

_____

_____

_____

_____

_____

A composer is a person who writes music. This is your chance to write a song of your own! Think of a tune you enjoy. On a piece of practice paper, rewrite the words, putting yourself in the song. You might wish to "sing" about a certain event in your life, describe what you are like as a person, or include your entire family in the song. (For example, you could use the tune "Puff the Magic Dragon" and say something like "Zack, the sup-er stu-dent plays in a band...".) Don't forget to give this masterpiece a new title. Write the finished words on the lines above.

P.S. Don't be shy! Practice and then give a celebration performance in front of your family!

You will need: a pencil or pen

Delightful Dinnertime

Dinnertime can be a fun time to sit with your family. Surprise them at dinner tonight. Decorate your dinner table with name tags for each place.

What to do:

1. Choose a light-colored piece of construction paper. Index cards would also work.

2. If you have a big piece of paper, cut it into rectangle shapes (about 3" by 5"). Fold each one in half the long way. This way the paper can stand up.

3. Now write each person's name on the front of a card.

4. Think of something to draw on the tag — such as what you like about that person or what you think he or she does well.

5. Very quietly, place the tags at each place on the dinner table. Shhhh, don't let anyone see you with this dinnertime surprise!

You will need: construction paper, scissors, crayons or markers

Dreaming of an Island Trip

Imagine spending two days on a warm, beautiful island. Choose two people to visit this island with you. Why did you choose these two people? Talk with them about a dream trip to an island. What would the island look like? What kind of activities would you be doing on the island? Draw a picture of your island dream trip.

| You will need: crayons or colored pencils |

Now it's your turn to be in the newspaper. Pretend you have done the job of a hero. Draw yourself in the newspaper, performing your heroic deed. Be sure to write the caption below your face. A cause for celebration!!!

You will need: a pencil or pen

Fabulous Fortune

As you can see, this rainbow has a pot at its end — but no gold in the pot! Color in the gold, and then list or draw what you would do if you were lucky enough to find a pot of gold. Think of the many things you might do with your new wealth. Would you buy presents for your friends? Have a big party? Give money to people in need? Share your ideas with a grown-up. What would he or she do with the fortune?

■ You will need: crayons

Faces of Feeling

Our faces give clues about how we are feeling. Think about your mom or dad and how you can usually tell by looking at their faces if they are upset or happy with you. Draw your face in each space, thinking about how your face "gives away" your feelings. Then finish the sentences to see when you might use such faces.

I feel happy when _____

_____

I am angry when _____

_____

I feel afraid if _____

_____

I am sad if _____

_____

You will need: a pencil or crayons

Find the Feelings

Hidden below are different feeling words. These words describe feelings everyone has from time to time. As you find and circle each word, think about times when you may have felt that way. You will find words written horizontally(➡), vertically(⬇), and diagonally(↘). None of them are written backwards.

```
N  P  T  N  A  F  R  A  I  D
I  I  R  K  S  N  A  P  S  I
C  C  J  O  T  R  G  E  E  F
E  K  E  A  U  H  U  R  T  F
B  R  A  V  E  D  P  J  Y  E
D  P  L  O  N  E  L  Y  A  R
A  E  O  K  Q  S  O  L  S  E
T  F  U  N  N  Y  M  W  A  N
U  P  S  E  T  R  Q  A  D  T
I  N  R  H  A  P  P  Y  R  P
M  E  A  N  Y  P  S  P  G  T
```

SMART	ANGRY	LONELY	JEALOUS
NICE	HAPPY	PROUD	BRAVE
DIFFERENT	AFRAID	SAD	UPSET
HURT	SHY	MEAN	FUNNY

You will need: a pencil or pen

The Generous Genie

In make-believe stories, a genie can grant wishes. Pretend you have discovered a magic lamp. Once you rub the lamp, a friendly and generous genie will appear. However, instead of wishes for yourself, you will be able to choose three friends and make wishes for them!! Write down the names of these lucky people and what you wish for them. You can draw pictures of them too, if you like.

| You will need: crayons, a pen or a pencil |

Friend #1 _____

The wish you would make for your friend

_____

_____

Friend #2 _____

The wish you would make for your friend

_____

_____

Friend #3 _____

The wish you would make for your friend

_____

_____

A Gentle Giant

In fairy tales and other stories, giants are usually big and mighty, but sometimes they are also friendly and gentle. Have you ever surprised yourself and done something which made you feel "bigger," almost like a giant? Draw a picture of yourself when you felt this way. Then tell about this event on the lines below.

You will need: crayons, a pencil

Once Upon a Time...

Go for the Goals

Many people set goals for themselves. Challenge yourself to see if you can achieve the goals you set. Accomplishing your goals will make you feel fantastic! Try setting three to five goals to reach this week. Write them down on the lines below (a few ideas would be keeping your room neat, not chewing your fingernails, or brushing your teeth without being told). Then cut out this list on the dotted line and hang it up where you can see it each day. At the end of the week, check to see how many of your goals you have accomplished! Be sure to celebrate your successes! Good Luck to you!

You will need: a pencil or pen

- -

_____'s Goals for the Week of _____

1. _____

_____

_____

Congratulations!

2. _____

_____

3. _____

_____

GOOD JOB

4. _____

_____

5. _____

_____

A Grown-up Me

This is what I will look like as a grown-up. For a job, I want to

_____

I would like to _____ for a hobby.

When I'm grown-up, I want to live in _____ .

You will need: a pen or pencil, crayons or markers

Hearts Full of Love

This activity will fill you with love. You know your family loves you. Ask them what they *especially* love about you. Decorate the hearts below. Cut them out and give each person (family or friend) a heart and ask them why they love you.

P.S. Surprise the people and tell them why you love them too!!!

You will need: crayons, scissors and paste

MY HERO

What do you think makes a person a hero? What does a hero do? Draw a picture of a real person you think is a hero. This person could be someone in your family, in the news or in your neighborhood. Talk with a grown-up about why you chose this hero. Ask who they would pick as a hero. Don't forget to ask why.

You will need: a pencil, crayons and markers

Individual Inkspots

Did you know that no two fingerprints are exactly alike? Use your thumb and fingerprints to create an art piece below. After you press your thumb onto the ink pad, press it onto the paper. Make sure you keep still so it doesn't smear, and clean your fingers on a wet paper towel when you're done. Then use a thin-tipped marker to draw faces, whiskers, hair, scenery and other additions as you create.

You will need: an ink pad, a thin-tipped marker or pen and a wet paper towel

actress

Ladder of Love

_____'s

LADDER OF LOVE

There are many ways to show you love someone. Make a list of some of the people you love. Then, draw yourself at the top of the ladder above. On each step of the ladder, write the names of the people you love.

You will need: a pen or pencil

A Lucky Leprechaun

Four-leaf clovers have been said to bring good luck. This leprechaun has a huge four-leaf clover just for you. Draw a picture or write what makes you feel lucky inside the clover leaf.

You will need: a pencil and crayons

The Mirror Box

Let's discover how other people see you! This activity will show you how you are seen by the people who know you best. Each side of your "Mirror Box" will reflect how you appear in others' eyes. The box will tell quite a story about you!

1. Find some type of box (it could be a shoebox, pretzel box or cereal box). Get permission to use the box.

2. Cover the entire box with light-colored construction or notebook paper. Glue or tape will work on the box.

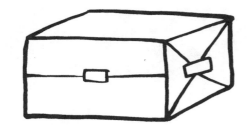

3. For each side of the box, find a person who knows you well. That means you will need to find six people altogether.

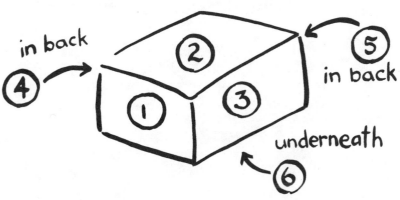

4. Ask each person how he or she sees you — what your strengths are, what you are like at home and at school, what kinds of things make you angry and happy, what activities you enjoy, and so on.

5. Have each person choose a side of your "Mirror Box" and write on it some words that describe you.

6. Once you have collected your "data," you can decorate the box. You could draw a picture of the person, or you could draw a picture of how they actually see you!

7. Once you have decorated and colored your box, it will reflect a lot about you.

You will need: a box, construction or white paper, tape or glue, crayons, a pen or pencil

SPECIAL PHYSICAL TRAITS OF _____

(Your name)

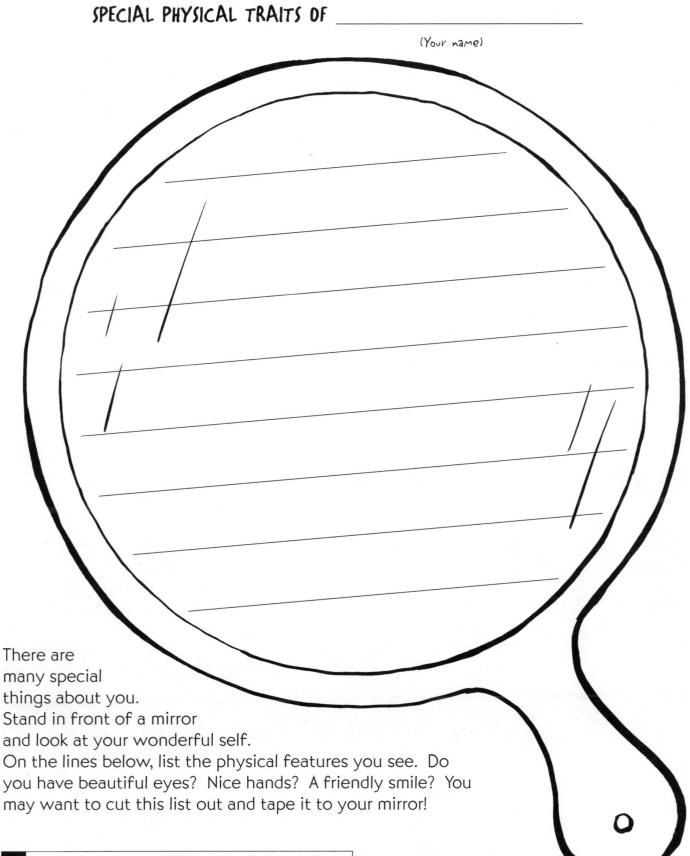

There are
many special
things about you.
Stand in front of a mirror
and look at your wonderful self.
On the lines below, list the physical features you see. Do
you have beautiful eyes? Nice hands? A friendly smile? You
may want to cut this list out and tape it to your mirror!

You will need: a mirror, a pencil and scissors

People Practice

Sometimes people say mean or nasty things. Spend some time with a grown-up you trust talking about how you could answer those people.

If someone says I'm stupid, I could say ...

_____

_____

If someone says I'm ugly, I could say ...

_____

_____

When someone laughs at me, I could ...

_____

_____

_____

When someone teases me, I could ...

_____

_____

If someone ever blames me for something I didn't do, I could ...

_____

_____

✋ You will need: a pen or pencil

A Personal Peek

I show love by_____.

I love to
_____.

I love it when my mom
_____.

With my dad, I love to
_____.

A person I love is
_____.

At school, I love
_____.

With my _____
I love to _____.

You have many feelings inside yourself. One of those feelings is love. Someone peeking into your heart would see lots of love. Finish the sentences above about love.

You will need: a pencil or pen

Picture Perfect

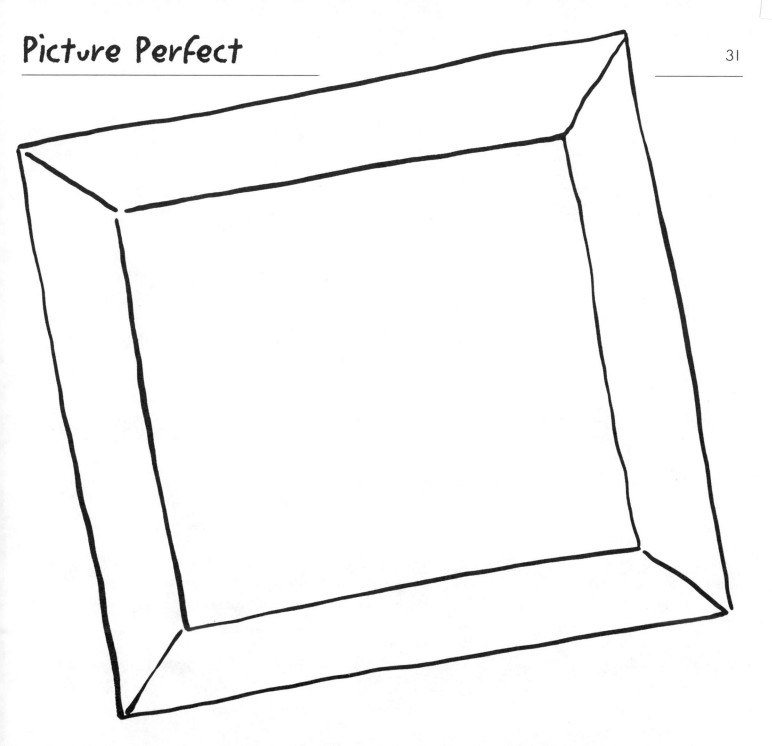

Do you have an oval, round or square face? Look closely at your features, then draw your face in the picture frame above. Be sure to include those things which make you special (such as freckles, dimples, beautiful eyes, long eyelashes, missing teeth).

Once you have drawn your special face, you will need a decorated frame to celebrate such a face! Use crayons or colored pencils to make your special frame one of a kind!

Variation: Mat and frame this unique face! Hang it up for all to see.

You will need: a pencil, crayons and colored pencils

There are many words to describe you. Try using the letters of your name to write a type of poetry called "acrostic." When you write an acrostic, your name is written vertically. The first word on each line begins with the letter from your name. There can be one or more words in each line. Sentences can be written on each line, or the whole thing could be one sentence. Here is an example of an acrostic:

E nergetic

M usical

I nterested in soccer

L oving

Y oung and sweet

Variation: Ask a grown-up to write an acrostic of your name.

You will need: a pencil or pen

Poetry Plus

Remember the name poems we did earlier? This time, you can write a poem using feeling words. Try making a poem from the following feeling words. You can write one or more words on each line. There also can be more than one complete sentence in the poem.

Example:

S ometimes I find myself
A lone and feeling sad, so I ask my
D ad to cuddle with me.

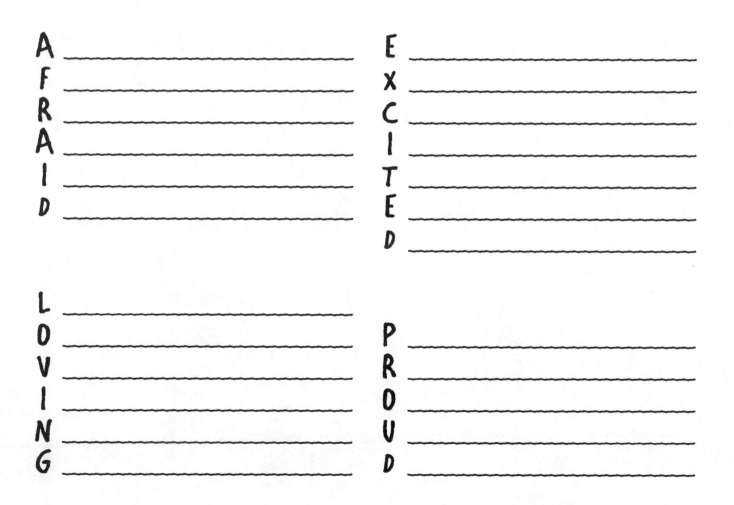

A _____
f _____
R _____
A _____
I _____
D _____

E _____
X _____
C _____
I _____
T _____
E _____
D _____

L _____
O _____
V _____
I _____
N _____
G _____

P _____
R _____
O _____
U _____
D _____

You will need: a pen or pencil

Pride Peak

Think of three very special things you are proud of and write them on the lines on Pride Peak. Write the most important one on the top line. Celebrate these accomplishments by drawing yourself on the PEAK of Pride Peak!!!

PRIDE • PEAK

You will need: a pencil and crayons

Pretend Person

If you could be someone else for a whole day, who would it be? Why? Pretend you could be anyone you wanted to be for one day. Draw that person in the space above. After you have finished, ask a grown-up who they would want to be. Ask them why they made that choice.

You will need: a pencil and crayons or colored markers

A Roller Coaster Ride

36

A roller coaster goes way up and then comes way down. Sometimes our feelings can do the same thing. At the top of the roller coaster, list five times you felt very happy. Then at the bottom of the roller coaster, list five times you felt sad. Draw yourself inside the roller coaster car after you've made your lists. Is there a smile on your face?

You will need: a pencil or pen, crayons or colored pencils

Things that make me happy

1. _____

2. _____

3. _____

4. _____

5. _____

Things that make me sad

1. _____

2. _____

3. _____

4. _____

5. _____

Roving Reporter

37

A roving reporter is a person who moves around from one place to another, gathering information. You can be a roving reporter as you conduct these interviews. Pretend that you have a microphone and become a roving reporter!!

Interview your family and friends. Ask them what hobbies they enjoy, what goals they have, what they see as their greatest strengths, and what fears they might have. Use this page and the next for your notes.

Don't forget to thank each of them for participating in your interview!

You will need: a pen or pencil

NAME _____ AGE _____

HOBBIES _____

GOALS _____

GREATEST STRENGTH _____

ONE FEAR _____

NAME _____ AGE _____

HOBBIES _____

GOALS _____

GREATEST STRENGTH _____

ONE FEAR _____

NAME _____ AGE _____

HOBBIES _____

GOALS _____

GREATEST STRENGTH _____

ONE FEAR _____

NAME _____ AGE _____

HOBBIES _____

GOALS _____

GREATEST STRENGTH _____

ONE FEAR _____

NAME _____ AGE _____

HOBBIES _____

GOALS _____

GREATEST STRENGTH _____

ONE FEAR _____

NAME _____ AGE _____

HOBBIES _____

GOALS _____

GREATEST STRENGTH _____

ONE FEAR _____

NAME _____ AGE _____

HOBBIES _____

GOALS _____

GREATEST STRENGTH _____

ONE FEAR _____

NAME _____

AGE _____

HOBBIES _____

GOALS _____

_____

GREATEST STRENGTH _____

ONE FEAR _____

Families enjoy doing many things. Draw a picture of your family enjoying a favorite activity or event together.

1. To begin, practice drawing your picture with a pencil on a separate sheet of paper.

2. Decide where you will place the cottonballs. They might make clouds, hair, food or another part of the picture which you will paint.

3. Draw the final picture on construction paper, paint it and then glue the cottonballs on.

You will need: construction paper, glue or a glue stick, a pencil, cottonballs and paints

Trace Your "Twin"

40

Sometimes it is hard to realize just how big you are. And you are growing bigger every day. In this activity, you can create your "twin" and see just how big you really are!

For this activity you will need:

- A big piece of butcher paper, another type of large paper or large cardboard box
- Someone who can trace around your body with a pencil
  P.S. You can also use washable sidewalk chalk to trace your "twin." Be sure to get permission before drawing on the sidewalk.
- Scissors to cut "yourself" out
- Crayons to color "you"

Directions:

1. Place the paper on the floor.

2. Carefully lie down on top of the paper.

3. Ask someone to trace around your body — not too close or else you will look too skinny.

4. Once you are traced, get up and color your new self. Color in the same clothes you have on today. Then cut along the pencil lines.

5. You may wish to hang up your "body."

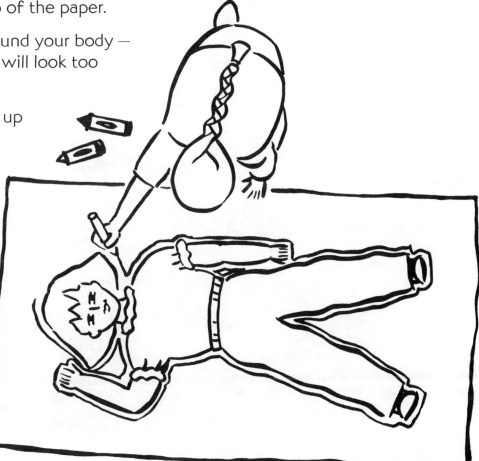

You will need: butcher or large paper to trace your body, a pencil, scissors and crayons

Try a Helping Hand

41

Everybody has things they do well, but everyone needs help sometimes too. When you need help with something, ask for a helping hand.

What to do:

1. Spread out your hand on this paper.

2. Carefully trace your hand with a pencil (this could tickle!).

3. After you have finished tracing your hand, write down on each finger a time when you might need to ask for help.

4. In the palm of your hand, write when you need help the most.

You will need: a pencil

You Are a Shining Star!

42

If you look up at the sky at night, especially if you are away from a big city, you will see a sky filled with stars. They twinkle, shine and shimmer. You shine in some ways just like a star! Think of the many things you do well. Draw a picture of something you do well in each of the large stars on this page. Use a light-colored crayon to color in the stars once you have finished.

You will need: a pencil and crayons

Do you have "prize winners" among your friends and your family? "Prize winners" are people who have helped you or done something special. These two pages contain four different awards for you to give to your "prize winners." Fill out the certificates neatly before presenting them. Have fun as the judge and award presenter!

You will need: a pencil, pen or colored marker

This award presented to

_____

for

_____

on this _____ day of _____, 19_____

Presented by none other than _____

Certificate of

_____

happily presented to

_____

on this ____th day of _____

_____

THE BEST _____ AWARD

PRESENTED TO

_____

BECAUSE

_____

BY

_____

ON

_____

FAVORITE _____ AWARD

PROUDLY PRESENTED TO

_____

BECAUSE

_____

ON THIS _____ DAY OF _____, 19_____

PRESENTER _____

Your Magical Memory

You have done many wonderful things with your family. Choose one time that you remember with special happiness. This could be a picnic, a hike, an event or a short trip. Draw a picture of this memory and then share it with your family.

You will need: crayons or colored pencils

Your Telling Tree

Did you know that a tree can tell a story? In this activity, you will make a tree that tells a story about YOU!! At a glance it will show all of your favorite things.

What to do:

1. Find a large piece of paper. Cut out or draw the tree trunk and the large leafy top of the tree. Make the leafy section big enough to hold several pictures.

2. Now that you have your tree, begin looking through magazines for pictures of your favorite things. Cut out pictures of foods, clothes, sports, houses, cars, smiles, pets, places and any other favorites you might see.

3. Before you glue these pictures onto your tree, find a picture of yourself to place in the center of your Telling Tree. If you can't find a picture, draw yourself in the center.

4. Now glue all of your favorite cut-outs around the picture of you. Try to fill the entire top of the tree.

5. To help your tree "tell" all about you, write your name on the trunk!

You will need: a large piece of paper, scissors, magazines, glue or a gluestick

Wishing by the Water

47

It is wonderful to be by the ocean. The sounds, the smells, and the miles and miles of beautiful colors of water all make the ocean a peaceful place to be. The seashells are always fun to collect, too. Pretend you found three huge seashells by the ocean and you could make three wishes. What would those wishes be? Draw the shells and write your wishes under them.

| You will need: a pen or pencil and crayons |

Take a look at a globe or map of the entire world. Notice all the countries and large bodies of water! If you could actually ride on a magic carpet, where in the world would you wish to visit? Why? Draw a picture of yourself as you travel to the country of your choice. Ask a grown-up you trust where he or she would choose to go.

You will need: a pen or pencil, crayons and a map or globe

ANSWERS TO ANGER: Have your child give you examples of times when he or she chose some of the strategies given. This activity is a valuable learning tool for children who struggle with their anger. Suggest one strategy to use the next time anger gets out of control.

BULLY BUSTER: Practice this activity more than once so your child feels prepared to cope, in a nonviolent way, with this uncomfortable situation.

LUCKY LEPRECHAUN: Discuss the many nonmaterial things for which we feel lucky. Encourage thoughts about family, friends, abilities and so forth.

A PERSONAL PEEK: Together, make up new sentences to complete. Try a different emotion.

PICTURE PERFECT: Mat and frame this unique face! Hang it up for all to see.

TRACE YOUR TWIN: It is also fun to double the paper and cut out two identical bodies. Color one as your front and the other as your back side. Then staple one vertical side shut, gently stuff crumpled up newpaper into your "body," and staple up the rest of the body. Now you have a twin person!!

TRY A HELPING HAND: Parents have bigger hands. Have your child trace your hand and do the same activity, showing that adults need to ask for help sometimes, too.

YOU ARE A SHINING STAR!: Discuss with your child the difference between planets and stars. Help your child draw the planets in relationship to the sun on a separate piece of construction paper. Help your child draw the planets from the sun. Add stars and discuss his/her strengths as you both work on this project.

PRIDE PEAK: Keep track of your child's accomplishments for a week. Have your child draw their own Pride Peak on a separate piece of paper. Then write those week's accomplishments on the new peak. You may wish to cut out the peaks as a reminder of these accomplishments.